3 *After* each of these notes write a *higher* note to form the named *melodic* interval
The key is F♯ minor.

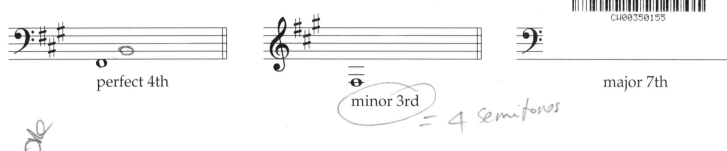

perfect 4th

minor 3rd = 4 semitones

major 7th

homework ✡

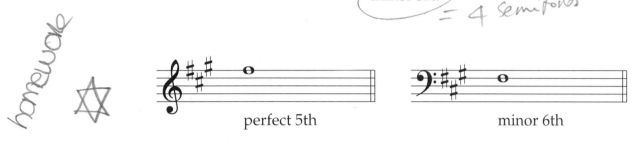

perfect 5th

minor 6th

4 Add the time signature to each of these five melodies.

10   7

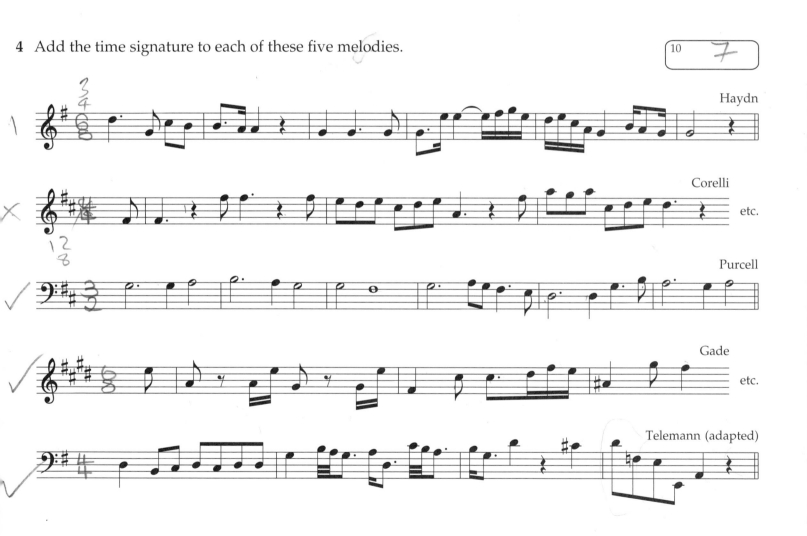

Haydn

Corelli
etc.

Purcell

Gade
etc.

Telemann (adapted)

3

5 Write as semibreves (whole notes) the scales named below.

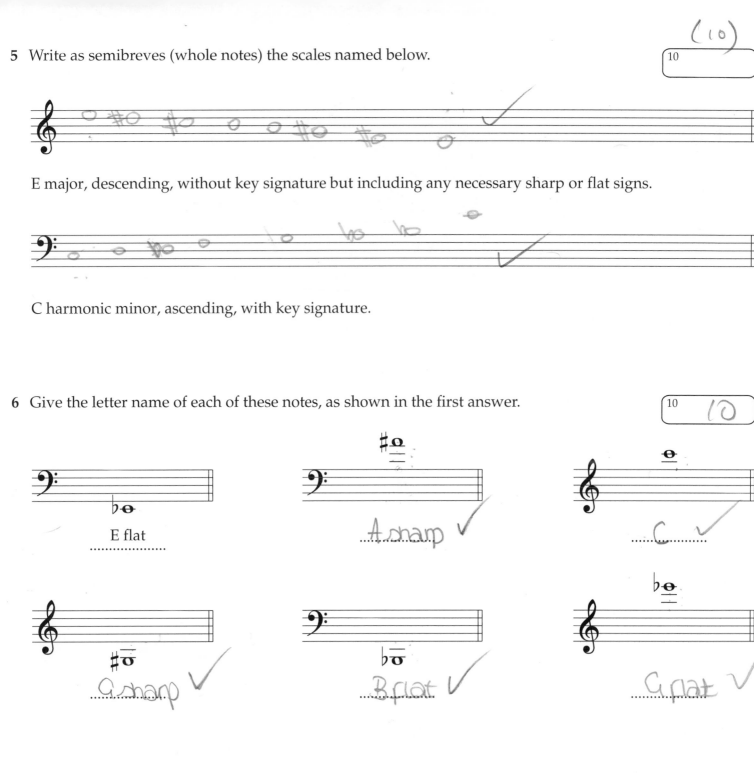

E major, descending, without key signature but including any necessary sharp or flat signs.

C harmonic minor, ascending, with key signature.

6 Give the letter name of each of these notes, as shown in the first answer.

10   10

E flat

A sharp ✓

C ✓

G sharp ✓

B flat ✓

G flat ✓

7 Add the correct clef and any necessary sharp or flat signs to each of these tonic triads. Do *not* use key signatures.

10   10

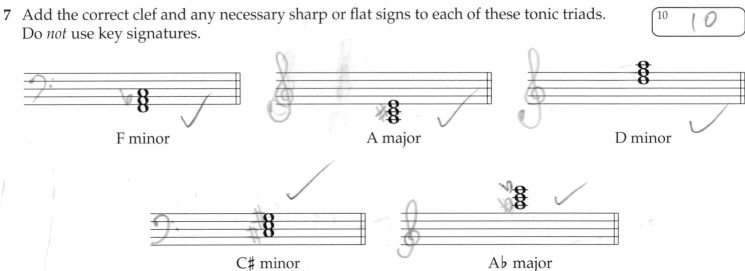

F minor ✓

A major ✓

D minor ✓

C♯ minor ✓

A♭ major ✓

4

8 Look at this melody by Mendelssohn and then answer the questions below.

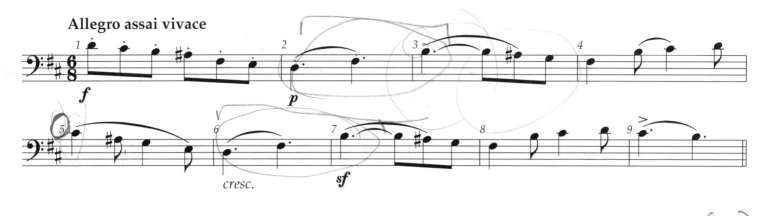

(a) Give the meaning of each of these:

assai ...Very...

vivace ...Energy, Lively...

the dots above the notes (bar 1) ...Staccato...

cresc. (bar 6) ...Crescendo...

sf (bar 7) ...Suddenly loud...

(b) (i) This melody is in the key of B minor. Draw a bracket (⌐‾‾‾‾⌐) over
three notes next to each other that form the tonic triad of this key.

(ii) Which other key has the same key signature as B minor? ...D major...

(iii) Name the degree of the scale (e.g. 4th, 5th) of the
first note in bar 5. Remember that the key is B minor. ...2nd...

(iv) Answer TRUE or FALSE to this sentence:
The tied notes in bar 3 are worth 8 semiquavers (16th notes) in total. ...True...

(v) Describe the time signature as: simple or compound ...compound...

duple, triple or quadruple ...duple...

(c) Write out the melody from the beginning of bar 5 to the end of the music,
an octave higher, using the treble clef as shown.

5

Theory Paper Grade 3   2012   B

TOTAL MARKS
100

Duration 1½ hours

Candidates should answer ALL questions.
Write your answers on this paper – no others will be accepted.
Answers must be written clearly and neatly – otherwise marks may be lost.

1   Add the missing bar-lines to each of these three melodies, which all begin on the first beat of the bar.

10   2

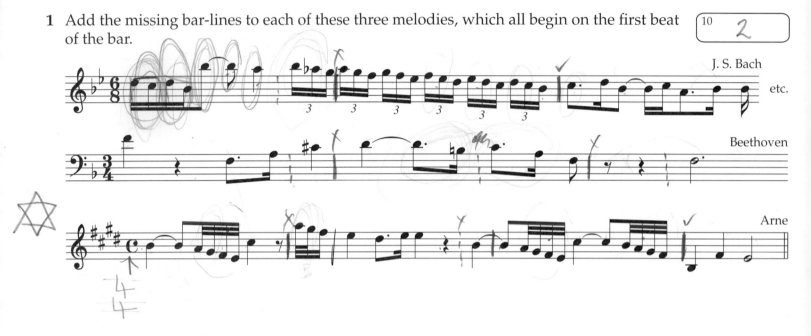

2   Add the correct clef and any necessary sharp or flat signs to make each of the scales named below. Do *not* use key signatures.

10   8

A major

F harmonic minor

3   This melody by Lyadov contains *five* deliberate mistakes.
    Rewrite it correctly on the given stave.

10   10

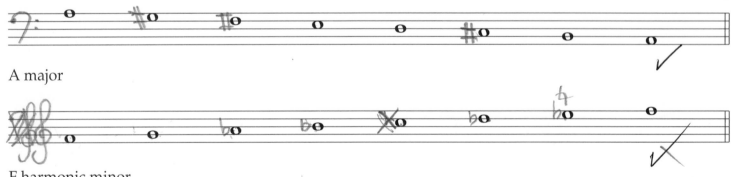

6

4 Write a complete four-bar rhythm in 4/4 time using the given opening.
  Remember to complete the first bar.

5 Add the correct rest(s) at the places marked * to make each bar complete.

J. S. Bach

6 (a) Rewrite the following melody with the notes correctly grouped (beamed).

Corelli

(b) Describe fully the melodic interval (e.g. major 2nd,
    perfect 5th) between the first two notes of bar 1. The key is G minor. ....major 3rd....

7 Write the key signature and tonic triad of each of the following keys.

C minor   Bb major   E major

B minor   Ab major

7

8 Look at this melody by Haydn and then answer the questions below.

(a) Give the meaning of each of these: `10` `10`

Allegretto ......fast slightly slower than Allegro ✓......

the **4** in **2/4** ......beats are crotchets ✓......

⌣ (e.g. bar 1) ......slur ✓......

p (e.g. bar 2) ......piano, quiet ✓......

:‖ (bar 8) ......repeat ✓......

(b) (i) This melody is in the key of E♭ major. Name the degree of the scale (e.g. 3rd, 4th) of the first note in the melody. ......5th ✓...... `10` `10`

(ii) Draw a circle around a note in this melody that is *not* in the key of E♭ major. ✓

(iii) Give the number of the bar that does *not* contain any note belonging to the tonic triad. Bar ...7... ✓

(iv) Name one similarity and one difference between bars 1–2 and 5–6.

Similarity ......The rythem's the same ✓......

Difference ......The notes are different ✓......

(v) Draw a bracket (⌐‾‾‾‾‾¬) over two notes next to each other that form the melodic interval of a perfect 5th. ✓

(c) Write out the melody from the beginning of the music to the first note of bar 6 *an octave lower*, using the bass clef as shown. `10`

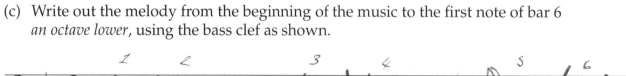

8

Theory Paper Grade 3   2012   C

Duration 1½ hours

Candidates should answer ALL questions.
Write your answers on this paper – no others will be accepted.
Answers must be written clearly and neatly – otherwise marks may be lost.

TOTAL MARKS
100

1   Add the time signature to each of these five melodies.

10

A. Soler

I. Albéniz

etc.

Buxtehude

etc.

L.-N. Clérambault

etc.

J. S. Bach

etc.

2   Write a complete four-bar rhythm in ⅜ time using the given opening, which begins on an upbeat.

10

3 Describe each of these melodic intervals, giving the type and number (e.g. major 2nd, perfect 8ve). The keys are named, and in each case the lower note is the key note.

D minor

E major

E♭ major

Type ....

Type ....

Type ....

Number ....

Number ....

Number ....

A major

B minor

Type ....

Type ....

Number ....

Number ....

4 (a) Add the correct clef and any necessary sharp or flat signs to make the scale of C♯ harmonic minor. Do *not* use a key signature.

(b) Write as semibreves (whole notes) the scale of B♭ major, descending, with key signature.

5 Name the key of each of these tonic triads.

  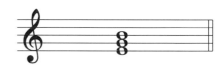

....

....

6 Transpose this melody *down* an octave, using the bass clef as shown.

10

Schubert

etc.

etc.

7 Add the correct rest(s) at the places marked ✳ in these two melodies to make each bar complete.

10

Mozart

Elgar

8 Look at this melody by Schumann and then answer the questions below.

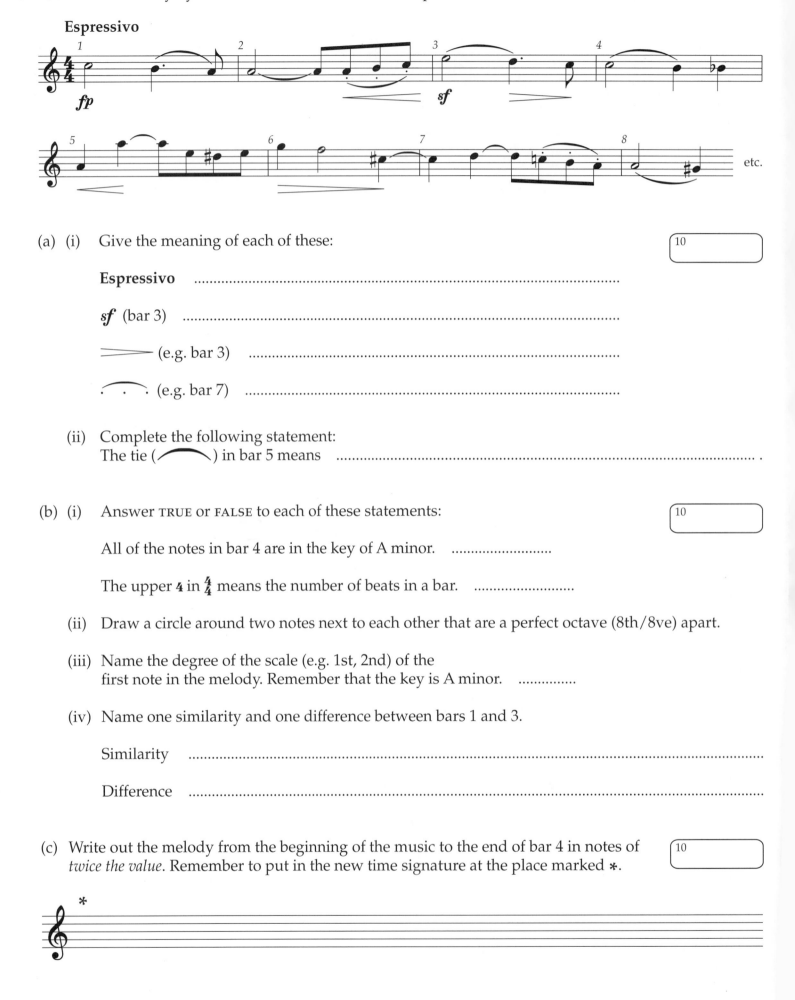

(a) (i) Give the meaning of each of these: 10

   Espressivo ....

   sf (bar 3) ....

   ⎯⎯⎯ (e.g. bar 3) ....

   ⌒ . . (e.g. bar 7) ....

   (ii) Complete the following statement:
        The tie (⌒) in bar 5 means ....

(b) (i) Answer TRUE or FALSE to each of these statements: 10

   All of the notes in bar 4 are in the key of A minor. ....

   The upper **4** in **4/4** means the number of beats in a bar. ....

   (ii) Draw a circle around two notes next to each other that are a perfect octave (8th/8ve) apart.

   (iii) Name the degree of the scale (e.g. 1st, 2nd) of the
         first note in the melody. Remember that the key is A minor. ....

   (iv) Name one similarity and one difference between bars 1 and 3.

   Similarity ....

   Difference ....

(c) Write out the melody from the beginning of the music to the end of bar 4 in notes of   10
    twice the value. Remember to put in the new time signature at the place marked ∗.

*

Theory Paper Grade 3   2012   S

TOTAL MARKS
100

Duration 1½ hours

Candidates should answer ALL questions.
Write your answers on this paper – no others will be accepted.
Answers must be written clearly and neatly – otherwise marks may be lost.

1   Add the time signature to each of these five melodies.

10

2   Write a complete four-bar rhythm in $\frac{9}{8}$ time using the given opening.

10

3 *Above* each of these notes write a *higher* note to form the named *harmonic* interval. The key is G minor.

perfect 8ve

major 7th

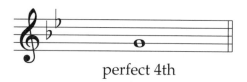

perfect 4th

minor 3rd

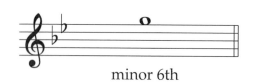

minor 6th

4 Add the correct rest(s) at the places marked ✳ to make each bar complete.

Britten

5 Add the correct clef and key signature to each of these tonic triads.

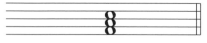

A major   F minor   Eb major

E major   B minor

14

6 Name the key of each of the following scales. Where the key is minor, state whether the scale is in the harmonic or melodic form.

10

Key ....

Key ....

Key ....

Key ....

7 Rewrite this melody using notes of *twice the value*. Remember to put in the new time signature at the place marked ✳, and remember to group (beam) the notes correctly.

10

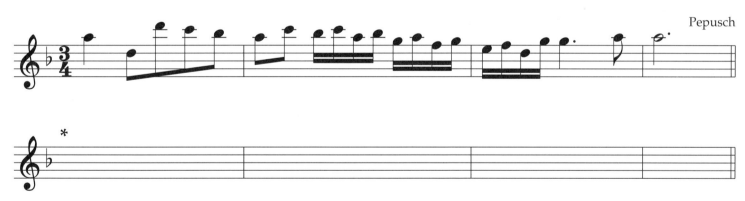

Pepusch

8 Look at this melody by Parry and then answer the questions below.

Andantino grazioso

(a) Give the meaning of each of these: 10

Andantino ....

grazioso ....

mf (e.g. bar 1) ....

dim. (e.g. bar 4) ....

rit. (bar 8) ....

(b) (i) This melody is in the key of F major. Name the   10
degree of the scale (e.g. 1st, 2nd) of the first note in bar 5. ....

(ii) Which other key has the same key signature as F major? ....

(iii) Name one similarity and one difference between bars 5 and 6.

Similarity ....

Difference ....

(iv) Answer TRUE or FALSE to this statement:
The lower **4** in **4/4** means quaver (eighth-note) beats. ....

(v) The first phrase has been marked with a square bracket (⌐‾‾‾‾‾‾⌐).
Mark all the other phrases in the same way.

(c) Write out the melody from the beginning of bar 6 to the end of the music   10
an octave lower, using the bass clef as shown.

ABRSM
24 Portland Place
London W1B 1LU
United Kingdom

www.abrsm.org

MIX
Paper from
responsible sources
FSC™ C109619

Published by ABRSM (Publishing) Ltd,
a wholly owned subsidiary of ABRSM
Cover by Kate Benjamin & Andy Potts
Printed in England by Page Bros (Norwich) Ltd
Reprinted in 2014

ISBN 978-1-84849-450-3

9 781848 494503